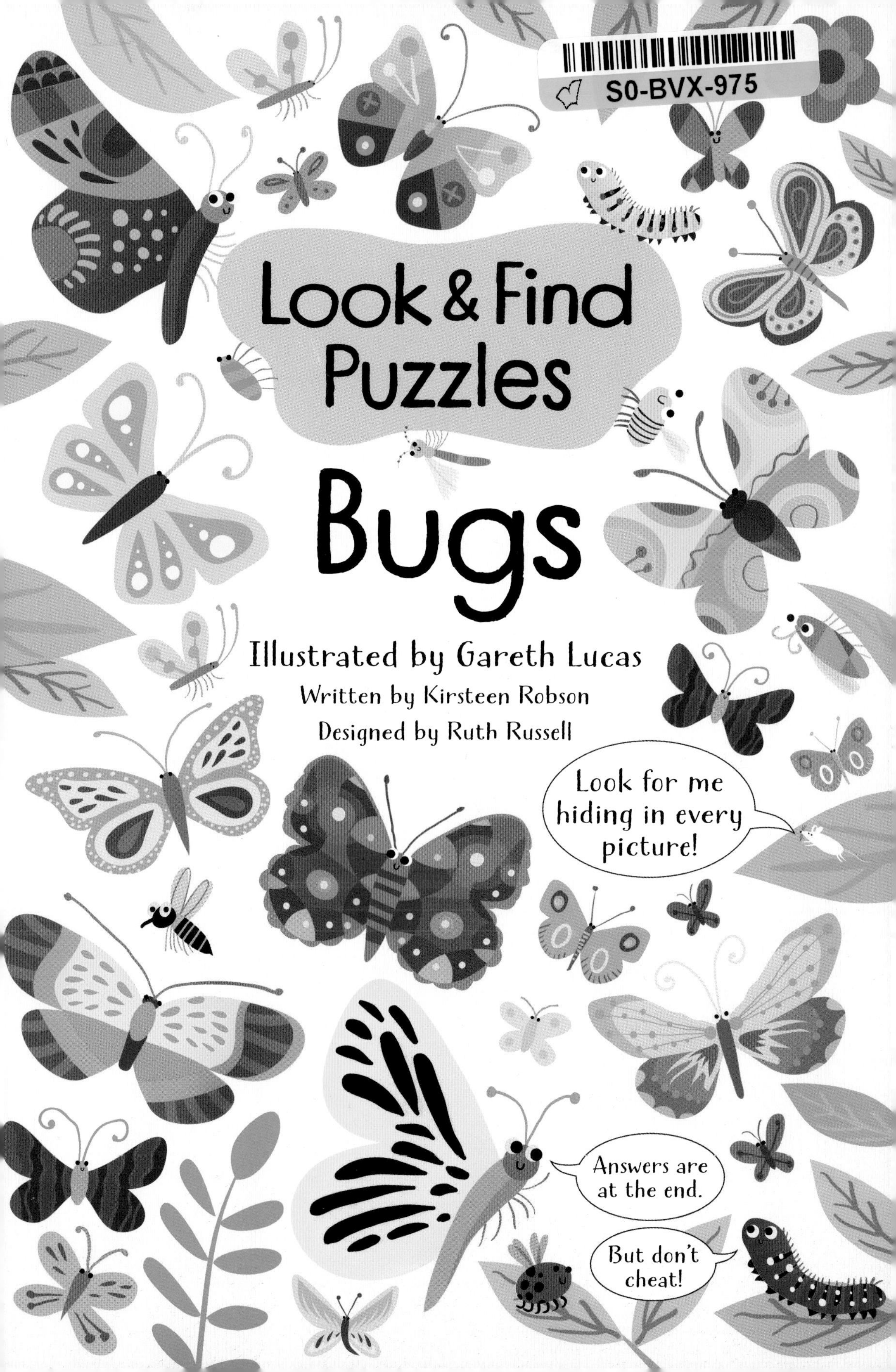
S0-BVX-975
Look & Find Puzzles
Bugs
Illustrated by Gareth Lucas
Written by Kirsteen Robson
Designed by Ruth Russell
Look for me hiding in every picture!
Answers are at the end.
But don't cheat!

Look for a caterpillar in a tent.
Can you find...
2 more bees
another bug the same as this

Can you see another bug just like me?
Spot a bug wearing brown boots.
5 other snails, all different
5 more flowers like this
another spider wearing a hat

Help me find our queen bee's crown.
Look for a bee on a bicycle.
Can you find...
another bee with three stripes
3 more jars of honey

Who's sitting on a swing?
one other pink bug like this
5 more baskets
another bee with a baby

Can you find...

5 other red bows

another 3 green caterpillars

Can you spot three butterfly cupcakes?
Look for a butterfly just like me.
2 more blue moths
another dragonfly
3 more butterflies like this

Spot a bug with a guitar.
Who's playing tennis?
Can you find...
2 more red spiders
3 other bugs just like this

Can you see a knife and fork?
3 different dice
another one of these
5 buttons, all different

Find a dragonfly flying a kite!
Spot someone riding on a broom.
Can you find...
a dragonfly that matches this one
2 other purple caterpillars

Who has picked a yellow flower?
5 more red bugs like this
another 3 pink water lilies
another bug like this

Where's my umbrella?
Can you find...
2 more bugs like this
3 other pairs of sunglasses

Spot someone playing a cello.
Who's got a drink with a straw?
another bat and ball
5 more blue flowers like this
another book

Spot two ants carrying a leaf together.
Can you see the only spider here?
Can you find...
1 more tiny bunch of flowers
another beetle like this

Look for an ant wearing boots!
1 more little present
2 other blue ants
3 more rakes like this

Where is the bug with the bags?
Look for an ant in a deckchair.
Can you find...
another butterfly like this
3 more wasps with green faces

Can you see a beautiful bird?
another hat like this
1 other scorpion
3 more of these flowers

Spot a bug reading a newspaper.
Who's got my other glove?
Can you find...
3 more hats, all different
another 2 flowers like this

Can you see two spider webs?
2 more wheelbarrows
5 other blue flags
2 more pink worms

Look for a rolling pin.
Where's my wooden spoon?
Can you find...
another 3 red spotted bugs
2 more chef's hats

Who has baked a hot pie?
6 other red-eyed flies
2 more flowers like this
another 2 mixing bowls

Find someone with striped socks.
Can you find...
1 more dangling spider
another 3 bees

Spot a spider with blue eyes.
Who's wearing a superhero mask?
5 more red, smiley spiders
another t-shirt
5 other bowls and spoons

Who's holding a frying pan?
Look for a butterfly with a trumpet.
Can you find...
5 more golden stars
another butterfl
like this

Can you see another heart like this?
1 more sunshine smoothie
another blue centipede
3 other orange caterpillars

Where did I leave my new scarf?
Can you find...
3 other black bow ties
1 more pair of these

Find two juicy carrots.
Spot three sleeping centipedes.
another green spotted bug
1 more hat
another 3 like this

Look for a cake with a candle.
Who else has a shiny pearl like this?
Can you find...
2 more moths like this
another 3 shooting stars

Who's got my flashlight?
1 other faraway bat
3 more bugs like this
another starry mobile

Answers

Cover

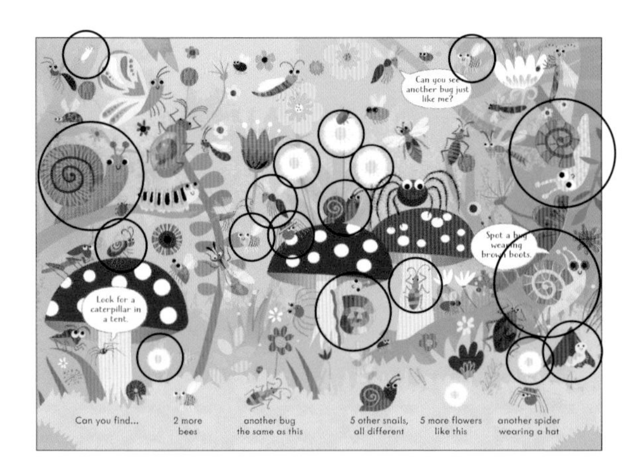

2–3

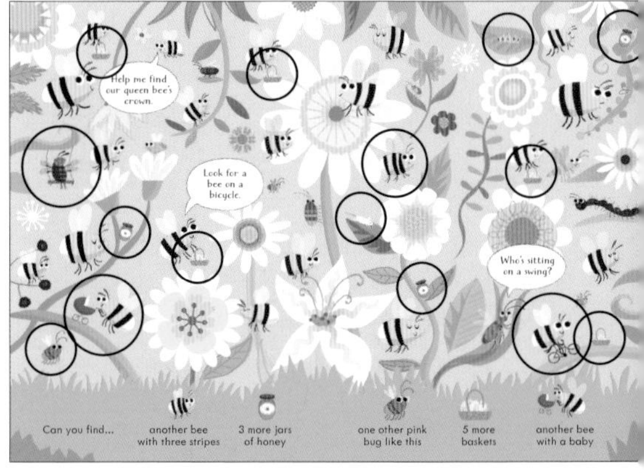

4–5

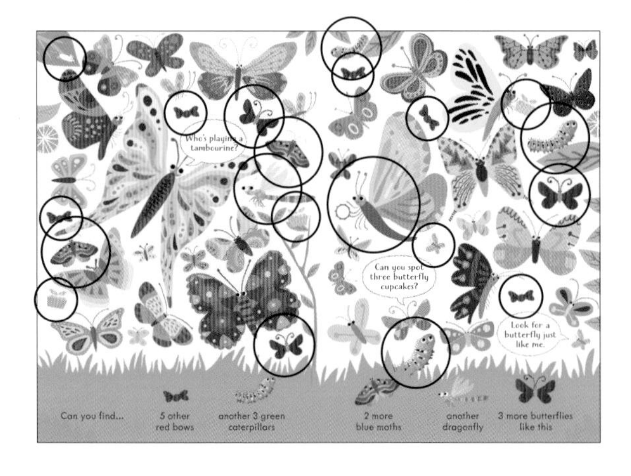

6–7

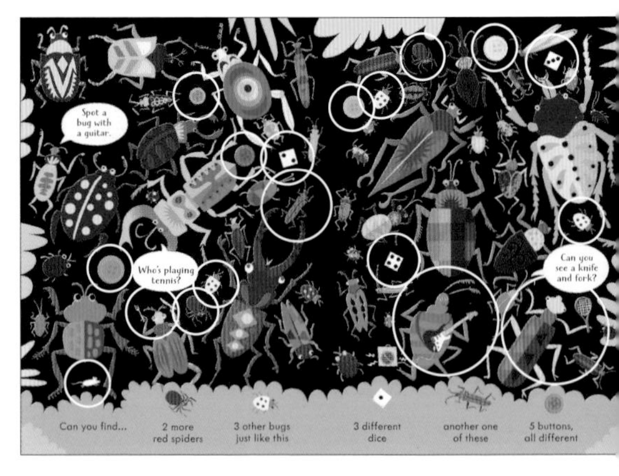

8–9

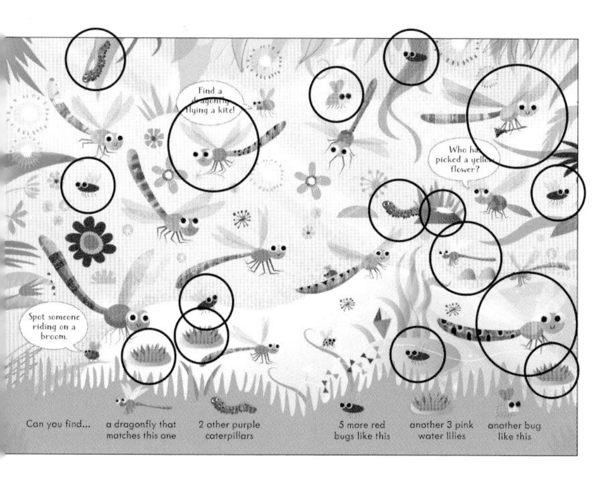

10–11

12–13

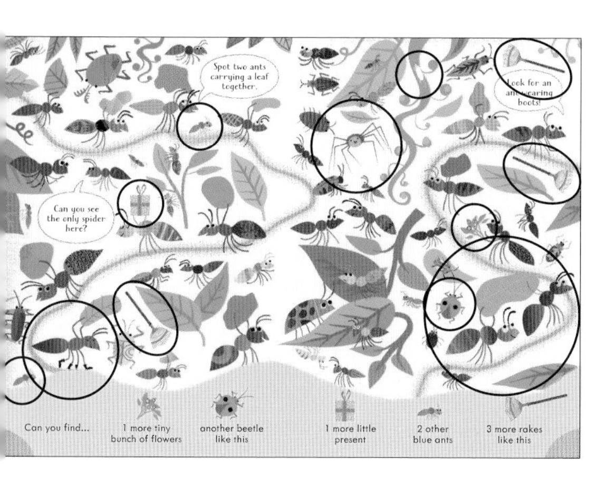

14–15

16–17

18–19

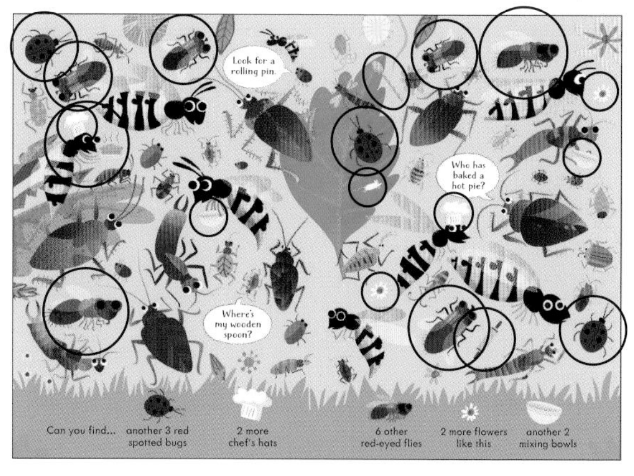

20–21

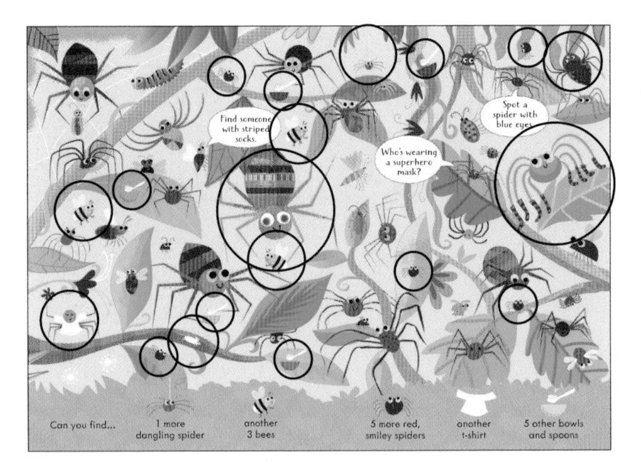

22–23

24–25

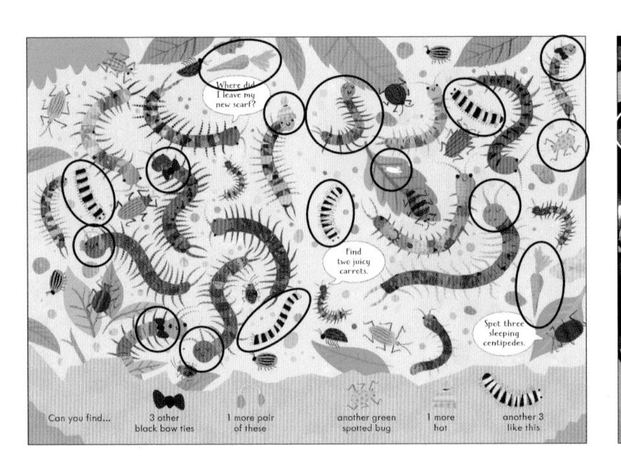

26–27

28–29

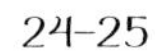

First published in 2022 by Usborne Publishing Ltd, Usborne House, 83–85 Saffron Hill, London EC1N 8RT, England. usborne.com © 2022 Usborne Publishing Ltd. The name Usborne and the Balloon logo are trade marks of Usborne Publishing Ltd. All rights reserved. No part of this publication may be reproduced, stored in a retrieval system, or transmitted in any form or by any means without the prior permission of Usborne Publishing Ltd.
First published in America in 2022, UE, EDC, Tulsa, Oklahoma 74146, usbornebooksandmore.com Printed in China.